A play by Bob Wilson

Farm Frights

Illustrations by Garry Parsons

Characters

Miss Bell

Miss Bell surprises everyone by getting a fright too.

Milly

Milly is cheeky.

Akbar

Akbar calls someone 'a baby'.

William

William is keen
to volunteer.

Katie

Katie thinks she knows
what she is doing.

Josh

Josh tries hard to
be brave but gets
scared.

Farm Frights

Miss Bell Now, it's our first morning at Ferns Farm Activity Centre so I'm sure you all want to go and explore. But first we've got some jobs to do.

All Oh no!

Josh What do you want us to do, Miss?

Miss Bell (*briskly*) For a start, someone needs to fetch a bucket of water so that we can do the washing up.

William I'll do that, if you like, Miss. Where do I have to go?

Miss Bell I think this leaflet tells us. (*She hands the leaflet to William.*)

William (*reads*) "Water for washing up can be obtained from the washroom tap at the back of the sheep barn."

Josh (*reading over his shoulder*) It says you go over that stile and across the small field. Then you go through a gate into the farmyard. The sheep barn is the stone building on your left.

William No problem, Miss. Leave it to me.

A few minutes later ...

Miss Bell That was quick, William. But why is the bucket still empty? What's the matter? Did you get lost?

William (*trembling*) No, Miss. I found the stile and I was going to go into the field but I didn't dare. It's full of bulls.

Miss Bell (*surprised*) Bulls?

William Yes. They're huge and hairy and they've got enormous horns and when they saw me, they started coming to get me.

Miss Bell I'm sure they weren't bulls, William. Farmer Ferns wouldn't put bulls into a field with a footpath running through it.

Milly They were probably just Scottish cows, weren't they, Miss? They have curly horns.

Josh And they didn't want to hurt him. They were just being nosey.

Akbar (*scornfully*) Fancy being scared of cows. You're a big baby, William.

William No, I'm not.

Katie Yes, you are.

Miss Bell	(*firmly*) No, he's not. He's just afraid of cows, that's all. Don't worry about it, William. Everybody is afraid of something.
Akbar	I'm not. I'm not afraid of anything.
Katie	Me neither. At least I'm not afraid of cows.
Miss Bell	Perhaps you would like to go and get the water for me then, Katie.
Katie	Okay, Miss. I won't let a few cows scare me.

A few minutes later ...

William That was quick, Katie.

Josh Where's the water? Did the cows chase you?

Katie No. I got across the field with no bother and I found the gate, but I was too frightened to go into the farmyard.

Miss Bell Why?

Katie There's a really ferocious dog there. It's huge and hairy and baring its big sharp teeth and barking. I'm sure it was going to bite me.

Miss Bell (*surprised*) But Farmer Ferns wouldn't let a fierce guard dog loose in a yard where visitors go.

William (*calmly*) Barking is just a dog's way of saying hello. It probably just wanted you to make a fuss of it.

Akbar (*mocking*) You're a big baby, Katie.

Katie No, I'm not.

Josh Yes, you are.

Miss Bell (*firmly*) No, she isn't. It's all right, Katie. Don't get upset. Everybody is afraid of something.

Akbar I'm not. I'm not afraid of anything.

Miss Bell In that case, would you like to fill the bucket, Akbar?

Akbar Yes, Miss. I won't be long.

A few minutes later ...

Akbar (*terrified*) Miss! Miss!

Miss Bell What's the matter? Why is the bucket still empty? Why is your T-shirt torn?

Akbar A kid tried to eat it, Miss!

Miss Bell (*surprised*) Tried to eat it? But we've only just had breakfast.

11

Akbar (*speaking fast*) I got past the cows and the dog but when I went into the farmyard, this kid just started nibbling me.

Miss Bell But all the children are here. What do you mean?

Akbar Not a child, Miss. A kid. A baby goat.

William But goats are harmless. They won't hurt you.

Katie Especially not baby ones. They're sweet.

Josh You're such a scaredy cat.

Akbar (*angrily*) No, I'm not.

Milly Yes, you are.

Miss Bell (*firmly*) No, he's not. He's just afraid of goats, that's all. Everybody's afraid of something.

Josh (*boasting*) **I'm** not afraid of goats.

Milly Me neither. **And** I'm not afraid of cows.

Josh **Or** dogs.

Miss Bell Then perhaps you two would fill the bucket for me.

Milly Of course, Miss.

Josh No problem, Miss.

A few minutes later ...

Milly Miss! Miss!

Miss Bell Whatever is the matter? Did the cows chase you?

Milly No.

Miss Bell Did the dog or the goat bite you?

Josh No.

Miss Bell What, then?

Milly It was all dark and spooky.

Miss Bell (*surprised*) But it's only
nine o'clock in the morning
and the sun's shining.

Milly It was dark in the barn, Miss. I don't
like the dark. It gives me the
shivers. I didn't dare go in.

Josh And I could hear horrible noises inside.

Miss Bell What sort of noises?

Josh Sort of shuffling and snuffling noises.
I think it might have been a ghost.

Miss Bell It's a sheep barn. It was probably just
some sheep you could hear.

15

Katie Sheep aren't scary, are they, Miss?
They're harmless.

William And anyway, there are no such
things as ghosts, are there, Miss?
They don't exist.

Akbar Milly and Josh are scaredy cats,
aren't they, Miss?

Miss Bell (*firmly*) No, they aren't. They're just a
bit frightened of the dark, that's all.
Lots of people are afraid of the dark.
Everybody is afraid of something.
(*Sighs*) At the rate we're going it
will be bedtime before we get the
washing up done. This time, I'll go.

A few minutes later ...

Miss Bell Arrrrrggghh!

Josh Are you all right, Miss?

Miss Bell It was in the sink! It was horrible! It was big and hairy and it was coming to get me!

All What was? What was it?

Miss Bell (*shuddering*) A spider!

William (*surprised*) You're not afraid of spiders, are you, Miss?

Miss Bell Yes. I am. I hate them.

Josh But spiders can't hurt you, Miss. They're harmless!

Katie They're only little.

Milly You're a scaredy cat, Miss.

Miss Bell (*firmly*) No, I'm not. I don't like spiders, that's all. Lots of people are afraid of spiders.

All Everybody's afraid of something.

Akbar But who's going to get the water now?

READY, STEADY, ACT!

Now that you have read this play it's time to act it out. You will tell your audience the story using words, actions and maybe some costumes and props.

CHOOSING THE PARTS

Choose who will play each part:

- Miss Bell is the teacher. She surprises everyone by getting a fright too.
- All the children start happy but are soon scared.
- Milly is cheeky.
- Katie thinks she knows what she is doing.
- Akbar calls someone 'a baby'.
- William is keen to volunteer.
- Josh tries hard to be brave but gets scared.

Who in your cast would be best at these roles? Read a few lines of the play to test this out. Make name stickers for your characters to wear.

Did you know...?
... Milk comes from cows, who make it to feed their calves. But we drink it instead.

SETTING THE SCENE

All the action takes place on a school trip to a farm activity centre.

Have you ever visited a farm? What did you see, hear and smell? What feels different when you are out of the classroom?

The children and their teacher are excited to be in a new place but don't know quite what to expect. Be sure to show your audience where you are and how the characters are feeling as soon as you begin.

Divide the group into two. One group sits on the floor and shuts their eyes. The other group makes a circle around them and makes noises that might be heard on a farm: animals, peoples' voices, tractors, weather noises like rain.

Then swap round. Could you imagine that you were really there?

WHAT YOU WILL NEED

Costumes

Dressing up can help you to pretend to be another character. Look at a picture of Miss Bell. What should you wear to create her character? A wig? Glasses? Sensible shoes?

The children can wear outdoor clothes such as coats, wellies and hats.

Props

Decide what props you will need. How can you make your acting space look like a farm? Perhaps you can make some fences or act in front of a whiteboard with a farmyard picture.

Sound effects

You can use lots of animal noises at the beginning of the play to set the scene. Can you make the noise of a tractor?

> Did you know…?
> … Dogs say 'woof! woof!' in English, but 'ouah' in French. Cows say 'meuh' and ducks say 'coin-coin'. As for chickens, they don't cluck, they say 'cot! cot!'

SPEAKING AND MOVING

Speaking

In this play, all the characters have to sound confident but then scared. Go through the play reading the instructions in italics for each character. Practise reading the speeches in a way that shows you are *boasting*, *shuddering*, etc.

It would be fun for each character to show that they are frightened in different ways. One of them could hide behind Miss Bell. One could cry. Collect lots of ideas and choose which one fits each character.

Moving

How do you stand when you are confident? How can you use your body to show that you are afraid? Can you strut? Can you stagger?

Practise moving as a frightened group when Miss Bell and the children go together to get the water.

WHAT NEXT?

Once you have performed this play you might want to:

- act out what actually happens when the children go to get water
- paint some farm pictures
- record your animal sounds to make a sound track.